From Dogpatch to Slobbovia

The **GASP!!** World of

Li'l Abner

as seen by David Manning White

with certain illuminating

remarks by Al Capp

BEACON PRESS   BOSTON

BEACON SERIES IN CONTEMPORARY COMMUNICATIONS
David Manning White, *General Editor*

FROM DOGPATCH TO SLOBBOVIA,
  edited by David Manning White

AGEE ON FILM: REVIEWS AND COMMENTS, by James Agee

AGEE ON FILM: FIVE FILM SCRIPTS, by James Agee

The main purpose of *Li'l Abner* is to make a living for me. The secondary and more celebrated purpose is to create suspicion of, and disrespect for, the perfection of all established institutions. That's what I think education is. Anybody who gets out of college having had his confidence in the perfection of existing institutions affirmed has not been educated. Just suffocated.

Some skepticism about the sacredness of all aspects of the Establishment is the priceless ingredient of education. Possibly those who read *Li'l Abner* will be discontent with the Establishment and make it a little better. And then in another time, another Capp, hopefully a better one, but no less peevish, will come along and point out how suspect and full of flaws that *improved* Establishment is, and so on.

My job (and the job of all humorists) is to keep reminding people that they must not be content with anything.

Al Capp

Welcome (-shudder!!-) Strangers!!~

This story isn't anything I made up. It is simply my rewrite of stories being told every day on our newspapers' front pages. Bigotry, it seems to me, is wholly a matter of geography. The paleness of the Caucasian must be a revolting sight in the lower-rent districts of Dutch Guinea, where folks are a normal, healthy black. But blackness is startling a few jet-hours away, where everybody is pink.

So, in this story I've substituted unfamiliar shape for unfamiliar color and with it examined the sources of bigotry.

Al Capp

THE
MOST
DREADED
DENIZEN
OF
DEEPEST
BROOKLYN
IS
"EVIL-
EYE
FLEEGLE"
MASTER
OF
THE
"WHAMMY"!!

FLEEGLE DOES NOT REALIZE THAT THE LITTLE JOIK IS **JUST** AS POWERFUL AS HE IS, IN HIS OWN HUMBLE WAY.

HE IS JOE BTFSPLK, THE WORLD'S WORST JINX. DISASTER COMES TO WHOEVER JOE IS NEAR.

WHAT ARE YA AFTER — MY **AUTOGRAPH?**

NO, SUH — YORE CIGAR BUTTS.*!!*

—WHEN AH HAS TO FISH 'EM OUTA PUDDLES!!*—SO, WOULD YO' KINELY DRAP 'EM IN HERE? AH'LL **ALLUS BE NEAR YO'**—

SO YA WANTA BE MY WALKIN' ASHTRAY?—*CHUCKLE!!*—OKAY, TAG ALONG!! WHAT **HARM** KIN YA DO?

This story is about characters who represent a sort of power this push-button age doesn't believe in any more: spiritual power. Fleegle's power, although evil, *is* spiritual. He has no reactors, no pushbuttons, yet his is a greater power than that we are now building great laboratories to discover. Will we, like the contemptible Fleegle, eventually discover that supreme power exists in the human mind?

This story also deals with the practical, everyday aspects of Love. "Shoiley" is proud to be the beloved of the man the world respects most at the moment — Evil-Eye Fleegle. Then along comes Milton, the astronaut, who is respected more. So Shoiley is prouder of being Milton's beloved than Evil-Eye's.

In the end, Mammy Yokum, whose spiritual power is greater than Fleegle's (because Goodness is nicer than Evil), takes over from Fleegle. But let me add a word. Although Mammy Yokum is Fleegle's implacable enemy, she isn't very different from him. She is simply as determined to make the world run *her* way as he is determined to make it run *his* way. And she wins because she's got more spiritual artillery. Neither of them consult the world as to how *IT* would prefer to be run.

Al Capp

*There's Nothing
Like a
Futuroid!!—*

HA!!

HO HO!! AH MADE A JACKASS OUTA TH' FUTUROID!!

CHUCKLE!!—AH WERE EVEN LUCKIER THAN AH DARED HOPE!!—TH' JEDGE GIVE ME 10 MONTHS!! BY TH' TIME AH GITS OUT, THEM PITCHERS WILL BE OUTA DATE!!

I hope this story never comes true.

The great fun of getting up in the morning, even to the men at Alcatraz, is that something you cannot predict may happen to you that day. Although we have laws on the books against gambling, life itself is an immense gamble — and let's be thankful for that. For once we take the element of unpredictability out of life, it will be hardly worth the time we spend living it.

If this story ever comes true, we will realize that the man who invented the Futuroid camera will have done more to make life unlivable than the man who invented the H-Bomb.

Al Capp

Kigmy

THE OFFICES OF KIPPER AND 'ERRING, THE AUSTRALIAN LAWYERS

HITS A CABLE FROM THOSE HAMMERICANS.!! THEY'RE SENDING THEIR BOY TO COLLECT THE FIFTY MILLION.!!

SEEM QUITE HEXCITED, DON'T THEY?

RA-THER.!! 'OW WOULD YOU FEEL IF YOU 'AD A CABLE HINFORMING YOU YOU'D HIN'ERITED A COOL FIFTY MILLION?

CONFUSED.!! THAT'S 'OW I'D FEEL.!! OUR BLARSTED CABLE DIDN'T SYE FIFTY MILLION WHAT.!!

COULDN'T SYE IT.!! I USED HUP THE TEN WORDS WHEN I CAME TO "MILLION". SOME 'OW I COULDN'T GET MY-SELF TO SPEND A HEXTRA SHILLIN' ON THAT HEXTRA WORD.!!

'OPE 'E DOESN'T MYKE A NARSTY SCENE WHEN 'E FINDS HOUT WOT 'E HIN'ERITED FIFTY MILLION OF.

LET'S FYCE IT.!! 'ERE 'E HIS.!!

KNOCK!! KNOCK!!

YO' KIN DUMP TH' FIFTY MILLION IN THIS BAG. AH IS TH' YOKUM BOY.

FIFTY MILLION IS A LOT (NO MATTER WHAT IT'S FIFTY MILLION OF) — WE CAN'T GIVE IT AWAY WITHOUT INVESTI-GATION.!!

HAVE YOU BROUGHT ANYTHING TO IDENTIFY YOURSELF AS A YOKUM?

OH, SHORE — AH ALLUS BRINGS SOMETHIN' ALONG T'PROVE AH IS A YOKUM.

FIFTY MILLION!! ONCE LI'L ABNER COMES HOME WIF **THAT**, WE WON'T **HAFTA** LIVE IN THIS MIZZUBLE, FLEA-BITTEN, LOVABLE OLE SHACK, **WILL** WE, PANSY?

NO, PAPPY.!!—WE'LL BE (GULP!!) **ASHAMED** T' STAY HERE AMONG TH' CHEAP, FAMILIAR, OLE THINGS WE **LOVES** SO WELL.!!

—AN' WE'LL BE TOO **RICH**, WON'T WE, T' ASSO-SHEE-ATE WIF OUR POVERTY-STRICKEN, IGGORANT, OLE FRIENDS WHOM IS DEARER TO US THAN LIFE **ITSELF**?

NATCHERLY.!! WE AN' THEM IS **THROUGH.!!**

WE'LL BE ABLE T' LIVE IN TH' **CITY** WHICH WE **HATES** SO MUCH— AN' EAT ALL KINDS O' RICH FOODS, WHICH WILL GIVE US **STUMMICK ACHES.!!**

RIGHT.!!—AN' WE'LL BE ABLE T' ASSO-SHEEATE WIF **REFINED** PEOPLE. —TH' TYPE WHICH DESPISES **US**— AND WHICH **WE** HATES WORSE'N POISON.!!

OH, (SOB.!!) EVERYTHING WILL BE SO **DIFF'RUNT** WHEN WE GITS THET ⊕★!!¬❋▢ **FIFTY MILLION.!!**

WE SHORE IS **LUCKY**— US PORE SOULS IS.!!

AH'LL BET THAR HAIN'T MANY LADS O' MAH AGE WHO HAS HAD TH' **BRAINS** T' INHERIT FIFTY MILLION.!!

YES, INDEED.!! YOURS IS AN UNUSUAL CASE, YOU UNFORTUNATE WRETCH.!!

THAR'S **PLENTY** O' THINGS A BOY KIN DO WIF A INHERITANCE LIKE **THAT**.

I COULD SUGGEST **ONE** THING TO DO WITH IT---

Last Will and Testament of Uncle Honeysuckle Yokum

On the eve of being hanged fo' murder, ah bequeaths to the Yokums mah Sure-Fire, It-never-Fails plan fo' Peace.

The reason all other plans has flopped is becuz they is based on a laffable mistake—namely—that people **WANTS** to be nice to each other.

Nothin' could be wronger.

People wants to kick other people around. They loves it. It gives 'em a feelin of sooperiorty. The one ketch is that them which gits kicked, gits mad, and kicks back.

And there yo' has the cause of all Trouble, and War.

Now the Uncle Honeysuckle Yokum, Sure-Fire, Never-Fail, Peace Plan is **BASED** on the indispootable fact that people **INJOYS** bein mean to each other —if they thinks they kin git away wif it.

??—YOU'VE GOT 50,000,000 LI'L CREATURES WHO **LIKE** TO BE KICKED—AND **DON'T KICK BACK** ?

RIGHT!!—SOON'S ANYONE GITS MAD AT ANYONE ELSE—**WHIZ-Z!!**—A LI'L KIGMY AHSOOMS TH' POSISHUN, AN'—**BAM!!**—YO' LETS OUT ALL YORE FURY ON TH' KIGMY—WHO **LIKES** IT—INSTEAD OF ON A HOOMIN BEAN—WHO **DON'T!!**

IT'S THE BIGGEST THING OF THE CENTURY!!—THIS'LL BRING PEACE TO ALL MANKIND!!

NO DOUBT YOU'VE ALREADY RECOGNIZED ME AS "FLASH" MANGLEBUGLE, THE WORLD'S GREATEST PROMOTER. I'VE MADE **MILLIONS** SELLING PEOPLE THINGS THEY **DON'T** NEED!!—BUT, **EVERYBODY NEEDS A KIGMY!!**—I'LL MAKE **BILLIONS!!**

BUT, WE DIDN'T INTEND—

THOSE KICK-LOVING KIGMIES WILL ABSORB ALL THE PUNISHMENT MAN **USUALLY** INFLICTS ON HIS **FELLOW-MAN!!**—IT'S THE END OF **TROUBLE**—IT'S THE END OF **WAR!!**—TAKE MY CAR!!—I'M GOING TO **WASHINGTON!!**

WHUT **FO'**, "FLASH" MANGLEBUGLE ?

But Li'l Abner
was not caught
this time.

LAWYERS WERE STARVING TO DEATH — **GENERALS** WERE BEING LAID OFF BY THE DOZEN — THE BANDAGE AND LINIMENT INDUSTRY WENT **BANKRUPT.!!**

FRY MAH HIDE.!! THASS **BAD.!!**

MEANWHILE. IN THE VAST VAULTS BELOW — MILLIONS OF KIGMIES ARE GOING MAD FROM LACK OF AFFECTION —

oh.!! sob.!! — ef only thar was a size 12 foot **INSIDE** that.!! —

i'm going **STIR-CRAZY.!!** — i can't stand this any longer.!! every bone in my body is aching for a **KICK.!!**

LOCKED IN THE CELLAR, 50,000,000 KIGMIES ARE GOING STIR-CRAZY —

i can't **STAND** it any longer.!! i've **GOTTA** be kicked — i tell you.!! **KICKED.!! KICKED.!! KICKED.!!**

take it easy, Karl.!!

LOOK who says "take it easy".!! — Klancy, there, was the **LAST** one of us to be (yum-m.!!) kicked.!! **HE** can still **FEEL** it.!! no wonder **HE'S** happy !!!

you **SAID** it, Korwin.!!

just a minute, Kids —

there **AREN'T** 50 million of us here. there's **ONE MISSING.!!** KRIS KOLUMBUS.!!

HE always was an advent-chooruss soul.!!

he must of **BROKE OUT.!!** — out into the world of **PEOPLE** and **FEET.!!**

FEET.!! with **POINTED SHOES** — **WOW.!!**

STOP.!! you're breaking my heart.!!

LOOK.! — he came **BACK.!!** what did you **DIS-COVER**, Kris Kolumbus?

A NEW WORLD.!!

For thousands of years we've been trying to remove the inhumanity from humans. Well, it can't be removed and it is nonsense trying to. The trick is to give man someone to be inhuman to who enjoys it. The trouble today is that when psychiatry discovers those rare and useful people who love being treated cruelly, we try to cure them, instead of breeding more of them. What this country needs is a good five-cent masochist.

Al Capp

HOOMIN STUPIDITY !! ,

AND **NOW**—WHAT **IS** IT YOU CAME IN TO SEE ME ABOUT—AN HOUR AGO, MISS BOVAK?

A FRIEND OF YOURS IS WAITING, GENERAL BULLMOOSE—NAMED YOKUM *!!*

ALL US KIDS IN TH' 6TH GRADE GOTTA WRITE COM-PO-ZISHUNS—ON **"SUCCESS"***!!*

IT'S A GREAT COMPLIMENT, MY BOY, AND ALTHOUGH I'M A BUSY MAN, I'LL TAKE TIME OFF AND ACTUALLY **SHOW** YOU HOW I MAKE A BILLION DOLLARS *!!*

Lately, it's become the fashion to make the lives of successful people nightmares by sending school kids to interview them, and ask them how they became successful. Even I have been victimized in this way.

My prediction is that no successful man will ever tell any kid seeking the truth *the* truth. Not only would the truth terrify the kid, but I don't think that the successful man could face it himself, or that his lawyers could get him a light sentence.

In this story, here's what would happen if a successful man told the truth about his success. It is based on my observation that the really great fortunes are never made out of human needs, such as the need for buttons or bread. The great fortunes are made out of human stupidity and the unending need of the stupid to be swindled. Anyone who realizes this becomes the man who owns the world, in his time.

Al Capp

Are the great deeds that all of us know about necessarily the deeds that most greatly affected the world? Could it be that such trifles as the eating of an egg, the closing or opening of a door, the falling of a leaf, have had more effect on mankind and the fate of the planet than the bravura deeds in the history books?

I have the nagging suspicion that many of the great recorded events which were supposed to have changed the history of man actually didn't. And that there may have occurred unrecorded, forgotten, casual deeds which were the true turning points of history.

Pappy Yokum is hardly our idea of a world-saver, and eating an egg is hardly a glorious deed. Still, something like this might have happened somewhere, mightn't it?

Al Capp

"The
Adorable Snowman" –
a Slobbovian tale .

Other children all over the world, wait happily for Santa Claus, on Christmas Eve—

But, in Slobbovia----

PAGES FROM "*THE ADORABLE SNOWMAN: A SLOBBOVIAN TALE*"

On Christmas Eve, when other children are having the best time of their lives---

And so now the once Abominable Snowman is known as the Adorable Snowman !!

-he visits all Slobbovian kids and hugs them in his warm, hairy arms. That makes them feel wonderful !!-

He is, in fact, the Slobbovian Santa Claus. He's too poor to give gifts —but every Christmas···

And no matter how economically you do it, making kids feel wonderful is the true spirit of Christmas, isn't it?

THE ART OF AL CAPP
by David Manning White

Among the millions — or perhaps hundreds of millions — who have read and enjoyed *Li'l Abner* since its inception thirty years ago, few have voiced their appreciation of its creator so enthusiastically as John Steinbeck. About a decade ago, Steinbeck wrote an appreciative panegyric about Capp wherein he compared the cartoonist to Sterne, Cervantes, and Rabelais, among other immortals. Finally Steinbeck flatly stated that "Capp is probably the greatest contemporary writer and my suggestion is that if the Nobel Prize committee is at all alert, they should seriously consider him." Although Steinbeck is, of course, our latest writer laureate, the august literary judges of the Nobel committee have thus far neglected Capp.

In research which I conducted recently at the Communication Research Center of Boston University, we ascertained that the most popular comic strips, such as *Li'l Abner,* reach an audience of 50 million readers or more practically every day of the year. In terms of other popular entertainment forms, television, for example, one would have to visualize a Jack Benny or Danny Kaye being tuned in every single day, year in and year out, to achieve a comparable audience. For unlike most television programs, seen by millions one year and off the air a year or two later, the comic strip appears to be our most enduring popular art. Almost from its beginning, *Li'l Abner* became one of those comic strips that transcended the stereotype of the mass audience. Avidly followed by such diverse readers as Queen Elizabeth, Charlie Chaplin, and Howard Mumford Jones, *Li'l Abner* became in our time an authentic, flamboyant nugget of Americana.

For three decades Capp has regaled his readers with *dramatis personae* now as well known as most of our public figures. Probably more people in this country (or abroad) would recognize General Bullmoose or Pappy Yokum if confronted with their likeness than could identify Dean Rusk or Chief Justice Warren. This does not mean that the bulk of our citizens are lotus-eating simpletons, but merely that acquaintance with the denizens of Dogpatch is reinforced through daily encounters that probably stretch over several years.

I've been reading *Li'l Abner* almost daily since I was a senior in high school in 1934, which means that I've been "exposed" to Capp's sorrowful and sardonic comments on the modern world nearly 10,000 times. Multiply this by 50 or 60 — or is it 80? — million Dogpatch *afficionados*, whatever the true number may be, who like myself read this particular strip (among others) as part of the get-going-in-the-morning-ritual, and you begin to see the audience impact of a strip like *Li'l Abner*. Assuming that only 50 million readers followed the daily and Sunday exploits of *L'il Abner* (and this is a conservative figure), there are more than a *billion* readings of the strip month in and month out. All in all, *Li'l Abner* has been read probably well over 300 billion times!

Confronted with this image of an unprecedented audience, what is the cartoonist's perception of his role as a mass communicator? During the fifteen years that I've known and admired Al Capp and his work, we've talked about this particular question on several occasions. Recently, in an interview with Capp that I tape-recorded, I asked him how he as an artist talks to his vast audience. Here is what he said:

> The thought that is uppermost in my mind is always to make myself clear to as many people as I possibly can. I think that's why I chose the comic strip as a way of working, rather than the novel, or the theater, or motion pictures. First, within fairly loose bounds, the comic strip is the freest of all mass media. There are no stockholders to dictate your next move as you have in motion pictures; you have no sponsors to give you almost unlivable restrictions as you do in television. In comics, one has so many employers that while all their voices are important enough, none of them is crucial.
>
> So that within bounds of almost instinctive taste, you are free to fool with any idea that interests you. The trick is to see that the idea is stated clearly enough to be understood

by the greatest possible audience. I think that anyone who communicates or who makes his living by communication can measure his success in only one way, and that is by asking, with how many people does he truly communicate? To how many people does he say exactly what he wants to say?

A good many writers, social commentators, and pedagogues have "explained" what *Li'l Abner* really signifies. Capp reads or listens to all such analyses with the interest that any artist would take in observing that his work was worthy of someone's thought, although at times he must have difficulty in restraining the gargantuan laughter that is always on the periphery of his responses. Nevertheless, there is a basic philosophy behind the day-by-day travails of *Li'l Abner,* and rather than interpose my interpretation of what it is, I'll quote again from the tape-recorded interview with Capp:

My first thought is to be amusing enough, perplexing enough, so that I'll be read again the next day. I want to give enough pleasure that the reader will come back, but also I want to talk about the things that make the job fun for me to do. I do have some notions about the world and man that I want to submit to the strip's readers.

I think that man is interested in two or three things. He is interested in death; he is exhilarated by the thought of death. That's the basis of all the adventure of *Li'l Abner*. It is always a flirtation with death; it is always a triumph over something that we all know will eventually triumph over us. So that I think we get some escape in *Li'l Abner* from the final certainty.

I think people are also interested in love, every aspect of love. Most people feel themselves failures in love. In *Li'l Abner* there is also the failure to make love fantasies come true. But the clumsy, ludicrous, pitiful failures of the folks in Dogpatch make the rest of us, who are also failing to realize our own fantasies, feel a little less stupid and perhaps a little less incompetent.

I think we are all interested in one other thing, which might be called "fortune" or "power" — all that comes as a result of winning the game of achievement against everybody else who is playing it against us. Death, love and power are the three great interests of man. They are the sources of all the stories in *Li'l Abner,* mainly because there are no others.

I think the whole meaning of existence, the great reward for having lived through a day, is that the day isn't as bad as it might have been. I think that's one of the satisfactions people get out of reading *Li'l Abner,* that no matter how badly their day has gone, his went worse.

Time magazine, in its first cover story ever devoted to a cartoonist, observed that Capp fills a niche in comics comparable to Gershwin's in jazz, or D.W. Griffith's in the movies. Their reason for this accolade: "From an instrument which had seemed as crude and monotonous as a dime-store flute, he produces noisy bass blasts of comedy, a skirling of irony and satire such as the comic page had never known." I do not think that Capp would agree that the comic strip had ever been as crude and monotonous as a dime-store flute. His knowledge and appreciation of such gifted predecessors in the medium as Herriman, whose "Krazy Kat" deserves a preeminent place in the pantheon of cartoon art, or Milt Gross or Rube Goldberg, to mention only a few of the great cartoon masters, would preclude any such thought on Capp's part.

Capp is in the tradition of the great satirists *in* and *of* the American tradition. He is the spiritual heir of tall-tale-telling Davy Crockett, the dialect humor of David Ross Locke's Petroleum V. Nasby, or the fire-eating indignation of a Thomas Nast decrying graft and stupidity in the American scene. Along with his gifted contemporary Walt Kelly, Capp has been the only cartoonist to use his strip to comment on contemporary political affairs. From time to time this candor takes both Messrs. Capp and Kelly out of certain newspapers until an irate editor cools down. Once when this happened at the *Pittsburgh Press,* the paper received 14,000 letters of protest. Capp observed: "Who would have ever thought that so many people who like my comic strip are actually able to write?" But he was only kidding, because we know that Capp is consciously trying to produce what *Time* called "a new kind of writing — a mixture of prose and hieroglyphics which simultaneously stings the mind of the intellectual and reduces the simple subway rider to coarse guffaws." In short, to communicate with each reader on the reader's terms.

In the various sequences which I selected for this small volume of Capp's work, I wished to show how he deals with timely topics (prejudice, foreign aid and the space program) within the framework of his larger objectives. If there is one common theme that ties together all of the stories, it would seem to be the stupidity which encompasses most of us poor mortals. Whether it be the stupidity of bigotry, with the crop of bitterness it is now reaping, or Evil-Eye Fleegle's ignorance of the real world around him, or the stupidity that calls itself cunning diplomacy while it hides another weapon under a mountain, Capp's pen-and-wit ferrets it out.

Several years ago a noted psychologist, Dr. A. J. Brodbeck, and I spent several pleasant hours discussing the meaning of *Li'l Abner*. Our resulting thoughts were published in a volume titled *Mass Culture*, and I would like to recall one thing we said there.

Li'l Abner, although it may seem utterly fantastic, is not running away from reality. As a matter of fact, by *exaggerating* the reader's defenses against some very painful parts of American reality — such as bigotry, venality and megalomania — it shows us how ridiculous these defenses often are. If, as we believe, Capp gets us to see what hypocrites we are, and yet doesn't make us completely despise ourselves for being what we are, he is indeed teaching us something. Although Capp may archly proclaim that *Li'l Abner* entertains us because we are obviously so much better off than the people of the Dogpatch-Slobbovia axis, he is merely pretending to flatter our egos. Whether he likes it or not, his "hidden" didacticism educates us too.

As anyone who has ever known Al Capp will testify, he is a very engaging and articulate person, and in almost any conversation the last word is his. Perhaps it would be the appropriate way to end this book. At least it would be typical. In the recent interview previously referred to, I ventured the opinion that during the past thirty years he had demolished virtually every major institution on the American social scene. To this he replied: "All I do is suggest that nothing is perfect. This gets some people perfectly furious at me, and they complain they're being attacked — "

Very well, Mr. Capp, if you say so. But say that again, please, and keep a straight face.